Hotel

Polly Stenham's plays include *That Face* (Royal Court and the Duke of York's), for which she was awarded the 2008 Critics' Circle Award for Most Promising Playwright, the *Evening Standard* Award for Most Promising Playwright 2007 and TMA Best New Play 2007, *Tusk Tusk* (Royal Court) and *No Quarter* (Royal Court).

also by Polly Stenham from Faber

POLLY STENHAM

Hotel

ff

FABER & FABER

First published in 2014
by Faber and Faber Limited
74–77 Great Russell Street, London WC1B 3DA

Reprinted with revisions 2016

A CIP record for this book
is available from the British Library

Typeset by Country Setting, Kingsdown, Kent CT14 8ES
Printed in Great Britain by CPI Group (UK) Ltd, Croydon, CR0 4YY

ISBN 978–0–571–31991–6

FSC
www.fsc.org
MIX
Paper from
responsible sources
FSC® C013604

6 8 10 9 7

For Tom
1965–2015

Hotel was first performed at the National Theatre, London, on 31 May 2014. The cast, in order of appearance, was as follows:

Ralph Tom Rhys Harries
Frankie Shannon Tarbet
Robert Tom Beard
Vivienne Hermione Gulliford
Nala Susan Wokoma
Abdi Ntonga Mwanza

K.M. Drew Boateng, Darren Douglas, Damson Idris, Daniel Kobbina, Jonathan Nyati, Joe Shire

Director Maria Aberg
Designer Naomi Dawson
Lighting Designer David Holmes
Fight Director Kate Waters
Sound Designer Alex Caplen

Characters

Vivienne
fifty-five

Robert
fifty-three

Ralph
seventeen

Frankie
fourteen

Nala
seventeen

Abdi
fifteen

Pirates

Time

Recently

HOTEL

A hotel on a remote Kenyan island. Late afternoon.
The villa is clean and white. Minimal yet luxurious. It is
self-contained, one of only three on the small island. The
decor gives no clue as to the location.

The central space is a communal lounge area. There is
a sofa, a glass coffee table and a CD player. There is a
slightly raised level at the back of the room. A stage
within a stage. There is a window at the top of the back
wall. It can be reached by climbing up a bookshelf. The
window has a ledge where someone small could sit above
the action.

Exits lead to two bedrooms. The lounge area leads on
to a patio with a plunge pool. Beyond this is the beach.
When the characters face the audience their view is the sea.

There is the detritus of recent arrival. Sun cream. A book.
A half-opened suitcase. The family arrived this morning.

PROLOGUE

The sound of waves. Insects.
The stage is empty. After a few seconds, Ralph emerges
from the plunge pool. He stands dripping in the sunlight.
He stares out to sea. After a second Frankie pops up next
to him.

Ralph Ooo la la . . .

Frankie Holy Moses . . .

They take in the view for a moment.

Why is the sea always a girl?

Ralph I think you mean ships. Ships are always girls.

Frankie Why?

Ralph Why not?

Frankie kicks at the sand. Fidgety.

Frankie Race you there. To the shore.

She nods.

Ralph OK. Terms?

Frankie If I win, you . . . tell him. Tonight.

Ralph Fine. And if I win?

Frankie I'll let it go.

Act One

The villa.

*Fleetwood Mac, 'The Chain', blasts from the CD
player.*

*Robert and Vivienne are alone in the villa. Robert
gestures for Vivienne to come to him. She ignores him
and continues unpacking. Robert stares at his wife. She
won't meet his gaze. He flicks the music off.*

Robert I organised a surprise.

Vivienne Did you?

*There is the sound of Frankie and Ralph at the shore.
A sudden scream. Then laughter. Robert looks out to
the beach.*

Robert I wish he wouldn't push her. Look. He's too
rough. *Ralph –*

Vivienne Leave them alone. They aren't children.

Robert Ralph isn't. No.

Beat.

Look at what he's doing. He's holding her down.

Vivienne Frankie can defend herself.

She turns, to look. Ralph suddenly yelps, swears.

See . . .

She turns back to unpacking. Pause. He watches her.

Robert It's a sunset boat trip. Just us.

Vivienne ignores him.

There are dolphins apparently. Look.

He waves a printout.

Vivienne Look at me.

He does.

Do I look sick?

Robert No.

Vivienne Then I do not need to be consoled, or in fact cajoled, by sunsets and fucking dolphins. I don't have cancer.

Beat.

I have you.

Robert Do you?

She looks right at him. Pause.

Vivienne I don't know yet.

She starts searching for a charger. Robert watches for a moment.

Robert They said to go to water sports at five. So . . .

Vivienne Five?

She checks her watch.

Now?

He nods.

I hate fish.

Robert They're not technically fish.

She pushes the charger into the adaptor and then into a socket. It sparks violently. Shocking her. She cries out. Robert goes to her.

She turns away. He tries to touch her. She won't let him. She composes herself.
She turns slowly. Faces him.

Vivienne I told you they wouldn't work. We can't charge anything.

Robert It doesn't matter. We're on holiday. We don't need our –

Vivienne You used to be good-looking.

He steps towards her. She stays where she is.

Robert You still are.

Vivienne Bullshit.

Beat.

I used to fuck you in toilets. On planes.

Robert I remember.

He's closer now.
He seems about to kiss her. She lets him get close, then breaks away.

Vivienne Do we get a drink on this 'cruise'?

Robert Probably.

Vivienne Have you paid?

Robert They put it on the bill.

She sighs.

Vivienne We'll never get the money back then. Come on.

Robert smiles. She cuts him down.

The sun is going down. My phone is dead. There's no internet. And, to add small sting to sweating insult, you left my book on the plane. So, I'll go. But only because there's nothing else to do. And if it's a one-mojito-per-passenger scenario, I'm having both. Agreed?

He nods. She heads to the door. He picks up two towels and follows her. They swing the door open to reveal a young maid, Nala. She is holding a stack of neatly folded towels and two flannels that have been fashioned, origami-like, as swans. These balance precariously on top of the stack. She startles Robert and Vivienne.

Nala Turn-down service.

Vivienne Yes, of course. Thank you.

She enters the room. Behind her back Vivienne mouths 'Tip her' at Robert. Robert mouths back 'With what?'

Nala sets the towels down and turns around. They stop mouthing and smile inanely at her. Awkward pause. Then Robert turns and exits. Vivienne follows. The door closes.

Nala puts the towels down and takes in the villa. She hears the sudden sound of Ralph singing to himself on the beach. He is approaching the villa. She startles. Knocking over the stack of swan towels.

The swans are ruined. She tries to refashion them. It becomes obvious she doesn't know how. She takes the pile into the bedroom.

Ralph bounds in through the patio. He calls out to see if anyone is there. Satisfied the villa is empty he grabs a jar of coloured jelly beans from the minibar. He is about to open them when the view catches his eye. He puts the jar down. Untouched.

The sky is slowly becoming more golden. He pulls a tobacco pouch out of his pocket. As he rolls he starts to hum and sing to himself, 'No Woman, No Cry' (Bob Marley).

As he lights the cigarette he starts jiving a little on his own. It's unselfconscious, joyful. Unknown to him,

Nala is watching from the bedroom doorway.
He turns around. He startles.

Ralph Hello.

They stare at each other for a moment. She doesn't move.

What's your name?

Nothing. She just stares.

Do you speak –

Nala English?

Beat.

I do.

She has a heavy Kenyan accent.
Awkward pause.
They both notice a pair of Robert's swimming trunks on the floor between them. Slowly Nala picks them up. She folds them. Badly. Pause. Ralph is awkward.

Ralph Let me help you.

He goes to help her pick up the towels. She interrupts the action.

Nala Do you want some petals?

Ralph Excuse me?

Nala Petals.

She brandishes a bag of rose petals.

Ralph I don't understand.

Nala Rose petals. On your bed. Part of turn-down service. Do you want some?

Ralph No thanks.

Nala OK.

She gathers up the towels as if to go. Ralph misreads the action as offence.

Ralph Actually. Sorry. Yes. Of course I do. Why wouldn't I? Thank you.

She turns slowly. Sets the towels back down.

There were some on my bed when I arrived. Shaped like a heart. But then my sister jumped on the bed and . . . Did you do that? Was that you? The heart.

Nala No I started at lunchtime.

She spies another beach towel on the floor. She regards it. So does he.
He darts over and picks up the towel. He folds it. He puts it on the table. Awkward pause.

Ralph I'm in your way, aren't I?

The light in the room changes suddenly. They both turn to the view. The sun has started to set.

Wow! Those colours . . . Sharding out from the sun like that. Crikey.

Beat.

It's like the sky has split its skirt.
Clouds . . . akimbo.

Beat.

Which would make the sun the sky's . . . crotch.

Beat.

That was weird thing to say. Sorry.

He turns to her. She is watching him.

Do you get used to it, that, living here? Do you look out and think, oh yeah, another average Thursday sunset. Yawn.

She thinks for a moment.

Nala I don't know.

He thinks for a moment.

Ralph It's amazing that everyone in the world, living and dead, have looked at the same sun.

He turns, but she is gone. He turns back to the sunset. After a moment Frankie flings open the door. She has a bottle tucked under her arm. She is wearing a brightly coloured sarong like a cape.
Frankie sniffs the air.

Frankie Ah, the sweet stench of victory.

Beat.

And . . . fags. The Livids will be livid.

Ralph They don't care. Where are they anyway? I thought Vivi was going to have a lie down.

Frankie I saw them. They're on a . . . raft . . .

Ralph A what?

Frankie You know. A shit boat. She had on her politician face. You know. The one where her mouth looks a bit like an arsehole.

Ralph Amazing.

Frankie And he had on his making-the-best-of-a-bad-situation face. Where his eyes crinkle and his mouth seems full of –

Ralph does the face.

Cock. Exactly. Anyway, they looked a bit stuck. The tide's coming out. It's getting all . . . swampy.

Ralph Did they see you?

Frankie They shouted, but I pretended I couldn't hear them. Just waved back.

She waves and grins and stabs the air with a thumbs-up sign.

Ralph Brilliant.

Frankie I thought so. Even ten minutes without that awful . . . tension. Just fuck or break up, why don't you? Christ.

Beat.

Maybe dragging that raft thing back to shore will bond them. Team-building.

Ralph Is it safe?

Frankie They're less then fifteen feet off shore. You could wade back.

Beat.

Probably.

Ralph picks up the bottle from the table. He raises an eyebrow.

Frankie There was no one at the bar. Served myself.

He shrugs and pours them both a drink.

In fact, there is no one anywhere, haven't you noticed? The two other villas are empty. And I'm pretty sure I saw the manager getting on a boat earlier –

Ralph He's probably gone to pick up some other guests. Most come by boat, don't they?

Frankie I'm not surprised. That tiny plane was fucking terrifying.

Frankie picks up the CDs.

Such a weird selection. Fleetwood Mac . . . The Beach Boys . . . Destiny's Child . . . Do you remember the dance we made up?

Ralph No.

Frankie Yes you do.

She puts in a CD. Ralph startles.

What?

Ralph Someone's out there. I saw the top of a head.

Frankie You're paranoid.

Ralph I swear.

She turns. There is no one there.

Frankie (*in a sinister whisper*) Paranoid . . .

Beat.

Ralph Maybe we should check on them.

Frankie Who?

Ralph The parents.

Frankie They'll be fine. Anyway, the water sports boy was watching. He did look about fifteen, but I'm sure he's . . . trained or whatever. Fancy place like this. It'll all be safe.

Beat.

Besides. They wanted a 'desert island experience', didn't they? Or he did. I say let them have it.

Pause. They sip their drinks.

Ralph The maid is hot. Have you noticed?

Frankie I passed a hot one outside. You mean her?

Ralph Yeah.

Frankie Miaow.

Pause. She jumps up.

We're avoiding it.

Ralph What?

Frankie The horse in the room.

Ralph Elephant –

Frankie Whatever. You said if I won, which I did. You would tell him tonight.

Ralph I won, Frankie. And anyway –

Frankie Elephant shit. And you know it.

He hangs his head.

Oh cheer up. You'll survive it.

Beat.

Won't you?

She hits 'play'. 'Survivor' by Destiny's Child blares. She dances to it and sings along, shimmying around him until he's laughing and joining in. They do an extremely good synchronised dance they made up years ago. They finish, exhausted. Frankie stops, snorting with laughter. She goes to change the CD.

Ralph Put on – (*He sings a line from The Beach Boys song 'I Get Around'*)

Frankie (*deadpan*) Sorry, what?

Ralph Beach Boys. Classic tune.

She starts scaling the bookshelf. She is nimble. Quick.

Frankie So, what's your plan? Before dinner? After dinner? How about during dinner? 'Spice' things up –

Ralph You're not funny.

She turns. Hanging precariously.

Frankie I wasn't trying to be.

Ralph Careful.

Frankie I bet the view is amazing.

She turns to him. Nimble.

Look. He'll find out eventually.

Ralph How?

Frankie Things come out. And I bet her people are all over it.

Ralph Oh God.

Frankie Just be honest. It's better you tell him here where you'll have no choice but to ride it out. Trust me.

Beat.

And you never know, the truth might be better. In her eyes.

Ralph Are you mad? It's worse. It's weird. It's weird cubed.

She turns and pulls herself on to the window ledge. She looks out of the window.

Frankie Hell's bells. You can see across the whole island. It's tiny. There's a storm coming. Can you feel it?

Ralph shakes his head.

I can. The air's all . . . sticky.

She starts scaling down.

It's a bit lurky here, isn't –?

Ralph I know what you mean.

Beat.

Frankie Its good for Madam that we're here though, no? You can't avoid the papers at home.

Frankie shrugs.

Ralph Don't pretend it wasn't awful. The headlines. 'Minister's hubby in sexy selfie scandal– will she re-erect him?'

Frankie 'Mousetrap: Father of two caught saying cheese with trousers down.' Come on, that one was funny. Sort of.

She starts to circle him. Playful. Riling.

Just tell him . . . Bite that bull by the balls.

Ralph I will, OK, just –

Frankie When?

Ralph I don't know. Soon.

Frankie Wimp.

Ralph Twat.

Frankie Mummy's boy.

Ralph Pussy pirate.

Frankie Hypocrite.

Ralph Fuck off.

Frankie By not coming clean, you are, though. You're just the same as him, can't you see?

He can't answer.
They can hear the sound of their parents arguing as they approach the villa.

Go on. Prove me wrong.

The doors fling open. Robert and Vivienne enter. They are exhausted. Muddy up to their knees.

Have fun?

Vivienne A shower. All I want is a shower.

She exits towards one of the bedrooms.

Frankie Was she not into it?

Robert There were no dolphins. There was no boat. It was a raft. Or more accurately, a floating bit of wood. The entire operation was run by a teenage boy who couldn't speak English. We got stuck on one of the swamp flats. I lost my sunglasses. Your mother became convinced there were reptiles in the mud. I tried to make the best of it.

Beat.

Which seemed to only piss her off more.

Beat.

On our way back I went to complain to the manager, only to be told by the maid he's gone to the mainland to collect another guest.

Beat.

I know we wanted somewhere remote. But this is . . . There's no one else here.

Robert notices the half-empty bottle. He looks at it, then at both of his children. He points at the bottle.

Explain.

Pause.

Ralph It's mine.

Robert From where?

Ralph Duty free.

Robert Don't lie.

Ralph I'm not.

Robert Yes you are.

He checks the minibar.

Who took . . .

He spies them on the table. He brandishes the jar of jelly beans in the air.

What have I told you both about the minibar?

Ralph For fuck's sake, I didn't even open them.

Robert We brought snacks with us specifically so we didn't –

Ralph Frankie ate them all on the plane.

Robert Regardless. I do not live in a world where it's OK to spend ten quid, no thirteen quid, on jelly beans.

Ralph Look about, Father. Yes you do.

Small pause. Robert checks the rest of the minibar. It's intact.

Frankie Oh no.

Robert Thank you, Frankie. Right. Where did you get it then? If it wasn't from here?

Beat.

Did you steal it?

Ralph Steal it?

Robert You don't have any money, so how else did you –

Ralph Well, how would you define theft exactly –

Robert I will not be lured into –

Ralph What?

Robert Semantics. Answer me –

Ralph Fine. I stole it. From the bar.

Robert Why did you lie?

Small pause.

The staff will be blamed for stealing this. Someone will probably be fired. Did that not occur to you?

Ralph shrugs.

What the hell is wrong with you? You'll pay for it. Yourself. At commercial value. Though pay with what exactly I don't know.

Ralph I'll pay. Although. I suppose that now it's mine, I can legitimately drink the rest.

He goes for the bottle. Robert blocks him, and hisses:

Robert I know things have been tough. I'm not an idiot, I know I have disappointed you, and I expect a degree of kicking out. But the rules aren't off. I am still your father. You are still my son. So behave. This holiday is for your mother. She deserves to relax –

Frankie is trying to slide out of the room. She knocks something over. Pause. She looks up shiftily. Swaying. Her father stares at her. He's realising she's drunk. He looks at the amount gone from the bottle, then at his two children.

Oh no, you didn't –

He turns to Ralph.

How much has she had?

Ralph She's her own person, what she drinks has nothing to –

Robert You were in charge.

Ralph That just shows, frankly, how little you know of our dynamic.

Robert She's fourteen, Ralph. When it's just the two –

Ralph Why are you talking to me about her? She's in the room. It's patronising. Talk to her.

Robert Frances. Come here –

At that moment Vivienne enters in a dressing gown with a towel around her head. Frankie takes the opportunity to dart out of the room.

FRANCES . . .

Frankie (*offstage*) I'm having a shower.

Ralph exits to a bedroom.

Robert Where are you going?

Ralph I'm getting dressed.

He slips from the room before Robert can stop him. Vivienne starts combing her wet hair. Robert watches his wife. They are silent for a few moments. She turns and looks out at the darkening sky. He comes up to where she is standing.

Robert What are you looking at?

Vivienne Malaysia.

He guides her hand. She lets him.

Indonesia.

Robert points her hand to the left.

Then . . . Somalia.

To the right.

Tanzania.

Robert Such beautiful names. Silken.

She steps away from him.

Vivienne What were you arguing about?

Robert Nothing.

Vivienne I heard loud voices.

Robert Unpacking. They're too messy.

Vivienne And you wonder.

Robert Wonder what?

Vivienne Wonder why they get angry.

Robert What do you mean?

During this exchange she has selected a dress from her bag. She slips it on and fastens her necklace.

Vivienne Well. You're hardly in a position to lecture them about mess . . .

She turns towards him. She looks beautiful.

Are you?

She goes to him and turns round. He does up her dress. She turns and looks at him. He steps forward to kiss her. She steps away.

Robert How long?

Vivienne Excuse me?

Robert How long is this going to last?

Vivienne (*acid*) 'This'?

Robert Yes, 'this'.

Vivienne What exactly do you mean?

Robert You know what I mean.

Beat.

I didn't actually *do* anything. It seems that somewhere. Somehow, along the way, everyone has forgotten, what it actually means to *do* something.

Vivienne That's not the point.

Robert It fucking is.

Small pause.

Sorry.

Beat.

(*Softer.*) I never touched anyone.

Vivienne Irrelevant.

Robert Why? Why is that irrelevant?

Vivienne You were about to.

Robert You don't know that. For the millionth time. How could you know that?

Vivienne Well. Let's see. The email exchanges, the nicknames, oh God, the fucking nicknames . . .

Beat.

(*Ugly.*) I mean. How exactly did you dream those pet names up, Robert? Did you spin around from the computer one day, trousers sagging around your ankles and notice Tom and fucking Jerry were on television? Did that get you inspired? (*Acid.*) Did that get you hard, Robert?

Robert Don't –

Vivienne Was that, her, 'Mouse', really the best affair you could come up with? Dirty emails to a twenty-year-old with a tit job, someone you haven't even fucking met?

Robert It wasn't an affair. To have an affair, you have to actually –

Vivienne Do you? Because what exactly is the point of betrayal then? What moment? The first time you touch? Because I don't think it is. A whole series of decisions go into play before that's even possible. I don't think the point of betrayal is as crude or as simple as touching. I think it happens quite a bit before that. It's when you know that the person who loves you, if they were watching what you were doing, typing, saying. Would probably . . .

Robert We've been through this. I saw an ad . . . I'd had a drink or two. I clicked. It didn't feel . . . It was a misjudged flirtation, a distraction, practically a computer game. It wasn't real. You're real. We. Are real. Is it really worth throwing away everything we –

Vivienne Waking up to a pixilated self-portrait of your cock, splashed across the Sundays, Robert, is about as 'real' as a fucking nightmare can get.

Beat.

You're pathetic. That's the big . . . reveal. Not that you're capable of this. We all are. But that you couldn't avoid the . . . cliché. I fell in love with you because I thought you were different. Difficult yes. But different. Unusual. Strong.

He winces as if hit.

What a fucking fool.

Beat.

I suppose in a twisted way you've done me a favour. I can see you now. Properly. In all your weakness. In all your . . . screaming banality. Which is almost the worst thing about this whole sordid episode.

Beat.

If you're going to fuck up, Robert. And God knows we all do . . .

Beat.

Fuck up better.

Robert All I can say is I'm sorry.

Vivienne And what does that mean? Nothing really, does it? It's just a word. It's what people say when it's too late. It's a sorry little stick of a word. Slick with your spit at my feet.

Robert (*softly*) What can I do then, to make this better?

Vivienne The truth is, sometimes 'sorry' doesn't cut it. Sometimes 'sorry' just isn't enough. The irony is, as embarrassing as your 'indiscretion' is, it's not actually the thing that hurts.

She regards him.

You've always hated me a little bit for the way our lives panned out, haven't you? It's not really your fault. History dictates it. You never thought I'd be winning the bread and you'd be . . . plating it. You smiled and soldiered, but some resentment has clearly . . . built.

Beat.

Which does make me wonder if on some level you did it on purpose. You knew that, particularly these days, it isn't hard to get caught out.

Robert Jesus.

Vivienne So obviously the thought has occurred to me that your pathetic indiscretion might be more than it seems. That it might be a bit more sinister. That it might be, consciously or not, sabotage.

Robert You can't actually think that. Not really.

Vivienne I can.

Robert How?

Vivienne Because in your situation I don't know if I'd put it past myself.

> *Frankie enters in a towel. Her hair matted and tangled. She looks very young. She goes to her father and slides on to his lap. She hands him a hairbrush and Robert brushes her tangled hair.*

Frankie Do we have to go to the restaurant? Can't we just get room service?

Vivienne I don't think there is room service.

Frankie Oh.

> *Beat.*

I bet there is.

Vivienne No.

Frankie No?

Vivienne I want us to eat together. Properly.

Frankie But I'm so sleepy.

Vivienne Tough. I booked a table.

Frankie You booked a table? There are no other guests –

Vivienne Up. Get dressed.

Frankie But I don't know which bag my dresses are –

Robert I'll find them. Come on. And take off that bloody sarong.

> *They exit to the bedroom.*
> *Ralph enters. As they talk, Vivienne selects a shirt from his half-open suitcase and he wordlessly puts it on.*

Vivienne What's wrong with Frankie? She seems . . .

Ralph I think she seems fine, perky, even –

She looks at him. Seems to really take him in. He is unnerved.

Vivienne It's not worth it, you know.

He raises his eyebrows.

People make mistakes. He's not a bad man –

Ralph Why haven't you done anything?

Vivienne Is that what you want?

Ralph Shouldn't you . . . react? He humiliated you. Publicly. You had to resign.

Beat.

It's like you don't care.

Vivienne How can you think that?

Ralph But you don't seem –

Vivienne I'm talking. Just because I'm not crying, just because I'm not in bits on the floor, doesn't mean I don't care. It doesn't mean I'm not really . . . hurt. Would you feel better if I curled up and sobbed? I think you think it would be some sort of, I don't know, catharsis, but if I did that I don't know if I would be able to get up again. I'm so. Tired, Ralph. But I'm trying to be . . . brave. And sometimes bravery is subtle. It's in the small things. Like not always wearing what you feel.

Beat. She looks down at her dress.

Or feeling what you wear.

Frankie enters, ready for dinner.

Frankie Frosty cocktail, Mother?

Vivienne Why not.

She looks to Ralph.

Frankie They'll follow.

Vivienne gets it, she nods, and exits ahead of Frankie, who drops back.

Be brave, be strong, your Johnson is long.

She darts out. Ralph lights a cigarette. After a moment Robert enters.

Robert Can I have one?

Ralph You don't smoke.

Robert Not normally, no.

Ralph hands him a cigarette. They smoke for a moment. Unknown to them Frankie sneaks back in, scales up the bookshelf and hides on the windowsill. Pulling the blind in front of her. Robert takes Ralph in.

Is that my shirt?

Ralph I only brought T-shirts Do you want it back?

Robert No. It's fine –

Ralph I don't want it. She just. Wanted us to be –

Robert Keep it. It looks smart.

Awkward pause.

Why are we being like this?

Ralph This is civil. Isn't it?

Robert You know what I mean. Like we're at a bad dinner party.

He turns to look at him.

It's me, Ralph. It's still me.

Ralph says nothing.

I hated my father. Hated him. He was such a weak man.

Beat.

I didn't go to his funeral.

Ralph I didn't know that.

Robert You were a baby.

Beat.

I thought having you would change how I felt about him.
But it only made me hate him more. When you see how
vulnerable a baby is and you – Then you . . .

He tails off. Pause.

I made a mistake. I know that. And I've apologised. But
I will not grovel. I will not crawl. Come back to me when
you choose to.

Beat.

I hope. With all of me. One day you will.

*Ralph has been looking down at his feet. His shoulders
tense. Slowly he looks up.*

Ralph I have to tell you something.

Robert What?

Ralph It's bad.

Pause.

Robert You can tell me. Whatever it is. We'll work it out.

Beat.

You knocked someone up, didn't you?

Ralph No.

Robert Well then, it can't be that bad.

Ralph Hmm . . . I don't know.

Robert Just tell me.

Ralph One day I logged on to our computer at home. I saw in the search history the adult sites you'd been on. I was curious so I followed your virtual . . . footsteps. I saw the kind of girls you clicked on. The ones you tried to chat to. I wondered how far you'd go. So I used a fake picture, someone similar, set up a profile. I started following you online. I chatted you up. When you replied I responded.

Robert What are you saying?

Beat.

What exactly are you saying?

Ralph Mouse never existed. She. Was.

Beat.

Me.

Pause. Robert is taking it all in. When he speaks it is quiet. Shaky. But controlled.

Robert This is a joke, right? A bad joke.

Ralph shakes his head.

You're serious?

It sinks in.

Oh . . . God.

Pause. Ralph looks away.

Look at me.

He does.

Why?

Ralph It was a prank. It. I. It snowballed. I just wanted to see. What you would. Do.

Robert If that's what you wanted, why didn't you fucking come to me, Ralph? Why didn't you ask? Say?

Ralph I –

Robert Oh my God.

> *He rests his head in his hands.*
> *He is revolted. Small pause. He looks up.*

You don't. Do that to people. What kind of fucked-up game were you playing? We ate breakfast together every morning, Ralph, and all the while you had a . . . gun under the table. Friendly fire from my own fucking son? Jesus Christ, Ralph.

> *Small pause.*

I hope you understand that your 'prank', your little 'jape' . . . well, it may well have just ruined my marriage, it's just ruined your mother's career –

Ralph That's not fair.

Robert Yes it is.

Ralph I DIDN'T MAKE YOU RESPOND.

> *Small pause.*

Robert You're a clever boy. You can act like an idiot sometimes, but underneath it you're bright and you're not twelve and you're not in the Famous fucking Five so stop calling it a 'prank' and call a blade a knife. There has to be something behind this. Something more to it. To do something so. Destructive. What was it? A test? What? Some fucking Freudian –

Ralph No. I don't know –

Robert Why? Why would you test me? I picked you up from school every single day. I fucking packed your fucking lunch. I read you bedtime stories while your mother was stuck in meeting after meeting. It was *me*. I have been a good fucking father, God damn it. You, your sister, you've been my *life*.

Ralph I didn't think you'd fail.

Pause.

Robert You asked me the definition of theft earlier. Well, this. This is it.

Pause.

It was you . . . that . . . She was you . . .

He looks nauseous.

Were you on your own? Did Frankie know?

Ralph Only afterwards.

Robert Does your mother?

Ralph No.

Robert Was it you who leaked it?

Ralph No. *No.* I never meant for that to happen. Someone must have seen. Caught on. I would have never. I never meant for it to go this far.

Robert You . . .

Ralph What?

Robert shakes his head.

Go on. Just say it.

Robert Sick. Fuck.

Pause.

What business was it of yours? Any of that? My
marriage? My sex life, my *private* . . . Everyone. Even me.
Has a right to privacy. Has a right to flaws. Has the right
to fuck up. I resent. No. I despise this culture of everyone
knowing everything and everyone telling everyone
everything about anything. It's screwing people in the
head. Look, you're proof. What an ill thing to do. A sick
sick thing –

Ralph You're blaming your virtual adultery on modern
culture? Wow. Slippery.

Robert You should have been a man. Told me. Asked me,
even fucking hit me. But to disguise yourself. To lure –

Ralph Don't you dare lecture me about being a man.
Don't you get it? You're not the kind of man I ever want
to be. You're *weak*. The more powerful she got, the more
threatened you became. You couldn't handle her strength.
It intimidated you. Emasculated you. Which is *pathetic*.
You did a good job at pretending, but don't think I
couldn't see. I was there. You should have been stronger
than that. You should have been *proud* –

Robert You have no idea. Weak. You think I'm fucking
weak? I stepped aside, I stepped out of the ring, because
if I looked after you, she could make the world that little
bit better for the both of us. We thought you needed at
least one parent, so I . . . And you think that's weak? You
think that's fucking weak, Ralph?

  Beat.

Listen. I was bored. I was lonely. And I made one
mistake. But that does not undo, or negate, my fucking
efforts, my fucking sacrifices as a husband, a father. It is
not. It never is. That simple. I have *tried* –

Ralph Well your mind hasn't been entirely on the job,
has it . . . big boy.

Robert takes a step back. Silence.

Robert You are still a child. A scared little boy. Still pissing himself at night. Still hiding things.

Ralph (*quietly*) I never thought you'd fail.

Robert Well, I did. And you know what? People do. All you've done now is to fail me too.

Beat.

You used to be my son. You used to sit on my lap.

Beat.

What did you do with that sweet boy? You sanctimonious little prick.

Beat.

Were you pretending to be him too?

He exits. Ralph sits alone on the sofa. He buries his face in his hands. Slowly his shoulders start to shudder.
    Nala appears in the open door, she is pushing a laundry trolley. She watches Ralph.
    Frankie peeks out from behind the blind. She is about to reveal herself when Nala enters. Nala approaches Ralph quietly. Frankie stays hidden, watching.
    Nala slips her arms around the shuddering Ralph from behind. He startles. She whispers soothingly into his ear. He leans into her, sobbing. Their faces are close. Frankie grimaces and draws the blind.
    Nala slips a rag from her pocket and presses it to Ralph's face. He slowly becomes still.

Blackout.

Act Two

A few minutes later. Ralph lies turned into the sofa. It looks as though he's curled up asleep. Or pretending to be.
  Robert enters.

Robert I didn't mean some of the things I said.

Beat.

I'm sorry.

No response.
  Robert sits next to Ralph on the sofa.

Ralph . . .

He is reaching out to touch Ralph when Nala reveals herself. Robert startles.

You startled me.

Beat.

Would you mind coming back a little later? This isn't a –

Abdi enters, pushes Vivienne ino the room. Her hands are tied. He is pointing a gun to her face.
  Robert raises his hands slowly. Swallows. When he speaks it is shaky but controlled.

Our money and passports are in the safe.

Abdi pushes Vivienne roughly on to a chair.

The code is four-four-nine-five. It's in the bedroom.

Ralph hasn't moved. Robert turns to him.

Ralph?

Nothing.

RALPH?

> *Nala pulls out a handgun. She gestures for Robert to put his hands back up. He does.*
> *Abdi shoves Robert down next to Vivienne. Robert reaches for Vivienne's hand.*

Nala *(Somali)* *Gabar baa halkaas joogtay, meeday?* [There was a girl, where is she?]

Abdi *(Somali)* *Ma aqaan. Halkaan bay joogtay.* [I don't know. She was here.]

Nala *(Somali)* *Soo hel.* [Find her.]

> *Abdi exits.*
> *Vivienne reaches and tugs Ralph's shoulder. His head lolls into view. He is unconscious. Eyes rolled back into his head. Nala points the gun at her. She puts her hands back up.*

Vivienne *(rising panic)* What's wrong with him, WHAT HAVE YOU DONE TO –

Robert Vivi, calm down –

Vivienne Show me he's breathing, show me he's *fucking breathing*!

> *Nala puts her hand on Ralph's stomach. It moves with his breath.*
> *As she does, Robert stands and tries to edge closer to Nala unnoticed. Nala whips round, pointing the gun at him. Then Vivienne.*

Nala Sit.

> *It's tense. They could take her. They glance at each other.*
> *Nala steps forward. Vivienne backs down to sitting. Robert stays standing. After a moment of him not moving, Abdi re-enters.*

Vivienne Sit down. *Sit down*, Robert.

He sits. Nala binds his hands behind his back.

We'll tell you where everything is. No one needs to be hurt. Tell her where you unpacked it all. Our money, jewellery, traveller's cheques. Tell her where to look.

Nala binds the unconscious Ralph. His head lolls.

Robert There's jewellery in that suitcase and there's cash in the drawer by my bed. The rest is in the safe.

Nala stops. Surveys her handiwork. She lights a cigarette. Her hand is shaking, subtly.

Vivienne Take anything you want. Take everything. Just don't hurt anyone. Please.

Robert The code is four-four-nine-five.

Beat.

Four. Four. Nine. Five.

Vivienne We won't report you. Just take whatever you want and go.

The blind twitches. A slither of Frankie can be seen. Robert notices. He tries to silently communicate it to Vivienne.
Frankie is trying to open the window and slip out of it. Her foot can be seen.
Frankie's exposed foot knocks a book off the shelf. Abdi panics and shoots at the wall.
Nala shoves Abdi, angry.

Nala (*Somali*) *Is deji fakin yahow, qof baad dili gaartay.* [Calm fucking down, you could have killed someone.]

Abdi (*Somali*) *Waa iga fakatay. Khaladkeyga maaha. Waa qori duug ah.* [It went off. It's not my fault. It's an old gun.]

36

Nala points to the corner. Abdi goes and crouches in it.
Nala goes to the bookshelf. She stares up at the
twitching blind.

Nala (*British accent*) Come down please.

Frankie stays frozen.

Vivienne Co-operate, Frankie.

Frankie whimpers.

Robert Do what she says, Frankie.

Frankie pulls open the blind. She is crouched, shaking.
Her position unintentionally mirrors Abdi's.

Nala Hurry up.

Frankie climbs down carefully. Nala extends an arm to
help her. Frankie doesn't take it.

Hurry the fuck up. Do what I say and I won't hurt you.

Frankie nods shakily. Abdi approaches with the tape.
She instinctively backs away. Abdi grabs her roughly.
Robert panics and struggles in his chair. He falls over.
The sound startles Abdi, who swings around and
points the gun at him. We see his eyes are wild.
Flickering. He is high. Breathing hard.

Robert Don't let him touch her. You touch her. Not him.

Nala (*Somali*) *Maxaa kaa khaldan?* [What's wrong with
you?]

She takes Abdi's face. She realises he's high.

(*Somali.*) *Waxbaad cabtay miyaadan cabbin?* [You've
smoked something, haven't you?]

He stares at her, glassy-eyed.

37

(*Somali.*) *Maxaan kuu sheegay? Waxaan kuu sheegay inaadan sameyn. Si wadajir ah u sameeya. Keliya yeel waxaan dhaho.* [What did I tell you? I told you not to. Keep it together, OK? Just do what I say.]

Abdi nods and lowers his gun and goes back to his corner. Nala takes the tape and binds Frankie as she speaks. Abdi fidgets in the corner. Fingering his gun.

Keep still. He startles easily.

Beat.

And I think he may have just smoked some crack. So . . . Softly softly.

She turns to them.

Understand?

Nala (*Somali*) *Toosi kici.* [Get him up.]

Frankie You're English. She's English –

Nala Am I?

Vivienne Frankie, please shut up.

Nala You can't help what rubs off on you. If you're dumped somewhere, you get dirty.

Abdi nods, approaches Robert. Frankie yelps, anticipating the worst, but Abdi only yanks him up and shoves him back in his chair. Frankie starts to sob.

Vivienne Frankie, it's going to be OK, I promise. We just need to do what they say. It'll be over soon and we'll get to go home. Think about home. It's all there. Waiting –

Frankie is crying harder now.

Robert Look at me, Frankie. It's a story. You're in a story you'll tell one day. That's all. A story.

Frankie stares at the unconscious Ralph. Scared.

Frankie (*shakily*) He. Looks. Dead.

Robert He's –

Frankie TELL ME WHAT'S WRONG WITH HIM!

Robert Frankie, *fucking shut up*! Please.

    Beat.

(*Voice cracking.*) Please.

    He looks at Frankie, then takes in Nala for a moment.
    She looks very young.

Where are you from? You must have a father? A mother, a sister? Imagine someone doing this to them –

Vivienne Robert, just –

Nala What did you say?

Robert I said imagine someone doing this to them.

    She turns and looks at him directly for a second.
    Then pistol whips his face.
    Blood runs from his mouth. He spits blood.
    Frankie looks at Nala aghast.

Frankie But you said . . .

Nala I said I wouldn't hurt *you*.

    Frankie is shaking. Nala watches her for a beat.

I used ether on Ralph. He'll be fine.

Vivienne What do you need? I'll double it. I'll call my bank. I'll do anything you want.

    Nala removes Vivienne's necklace. She holds it up to
    the light.

Nala Money? Money makes the world go round, right?

    She stares at them. They don't answer.

I disagree. It's not a means to an end . . . Money. It's just more shit. Isn't it?

Nala throws the necklace out of the window. Abdi watches hungrily but doesn't move.

(*Somali.*) *Kaamarada rakib.* [Set up the camera.]

Over the next small sequence Abdi sets up the camera so it is pointing at the back wall. One by one the family notice what he's doing.

Vivienne Where is everyone else?

Nala You should be thanking me.

Vivienne Excuse me?

Nala I thought you wanted a desert island experience? But you wanted it swaddled in Egyptian cotton. You wanted it slurping on a cocktail in a hot tub. You wanted to enjoy paradise from your patio. Skin pink from your shower. Safe in your linen shirt. The thing is. When you strip it back, the Egyptian cotton, the patio, the cocktails and the hot tub. Well, they're just props. Your reality here is just a stage set. It can be dismantled overnight. (*Somali.*) *Halkaas keen iyada hadda.* [Get her up there, now.]

Abdi shoves Vivienne on to the slightly raised platform. Frankie panics.

Frankie Mummy –

Vivienne Close your eyes, Frankie, OK, just close your eyes.

She does.

Frankie It's a story it's a story it's a story.

Nala picks up the video camera and prepares to film.

Nala You're there, and then you're here. And when I upload this you'll be everywhere. Amazing.

She aims the camera at Vivienne.

What's your job, Vivienne? Tell the camera.

Small pause.

Vivienne Well . . .

Nala Go on.

Vivienne I was the Secretary of State for Trade and Investment.

Beat.

Nala What do you mean, 'was'?

Vivienne I resigned.

Nala What?

Beat.

When? When did you resign?

Vivienne The day before we left. Two days ago.

Nala What's your position now?

Beat.

Vivienne If you're asking whether I'm important any more, the answer is no.

Beat.

That matters to you, doesn't it?

Beat.

Whatever this is. Whatever you want. You only have one chance to pull it off. If I were you I'd wait for someone with a bit more . . . currency.

Beat.

Frankie My godfather holidays in the Caymans . . . First week of the New Year. Like clockwork. He's the Prime Minister now.

Robert Shut *up*, Frankie.

Frankie It's true –

Robert Look. We can prove she resigned. It's all over the . . .

Pause. Irony dawns.

Fuck.

Nala It doesn't matter.

Frankie But she isn't important any more, she really isn't, everyone's been laughing at her, he's a national joke –

Vivienne I think she gets it, Frankie, thank you –

Nala SHUT UP!

She raises her gun.

Like I said. Irrelevant. This is about you and me.

Vivienne Then let them go. Keep me, but let them go –

Nala (*points to Frankie*) No. She needs to see.

Frankie (*nervously*) See what?

Nala The consequences.

Frankie What does she mean?

Vivienne (*softly*) I don't know.

Nala Because nowadays there's a big distance between action and consequence, isn't there? Which seems cowardly to me.

Beat.

At least when you colonised in the old days you had to actually go to the country with a gun. Unpleasant, definitely, but at least it was honest. You just rolled up. One hand on a rifle, the other clawing a pink gin. What a party you started. And are still. Having.

Beat.

In your way . . .

Robert What are you talking about?

Nala mock-raises a glass.

Nala The party . . . (*Somali.*) *Toosi.* [Get him up.]

Abdi drags Robert up. He positions him on his knees in front of Vivienne, and yanks his head back so he is staring up at her.

You had a whole country, forced to its knees in front of you, Kenya's lips parted, eyes wide, begging to be told what to do . . .

It got a bit sexy, didn't it? All that new land to play with. It must have been fun. Your party. So go on. Show me the fun. Show me the party. Get him to dance for you, go on.

They stand blankly.

Make him fucking dance for you. It's a party. *Fucking dance!*

Vivienne Dance for me.

He does. It is odd. Nightmarish. Vivienne can't look.

Nala Touch him. Touch him wherever you want.

Vivienne I . . .

Nala Under his clothes. Go on. He's yours now. Claim him.

43

Vivienne touches Robert tentatively.

Fucking grope him. Get your hands good and dirty. Go on.

She does.

Kiss him.

She does.

Slap him.

She doesn't move.

I said. Slap him.

She slaps him lightly.

Properly.

She slaps him hard. Robert yelps.

Then you fucked us good and proper.

Horrified beat.

But we just don't have time for that. So let's jump to after the fucking, when you just . . . left us. On our knees.

Beat.

It must have been quite the fucking because it's years later, and we're still buckled. But this time we're hungry too. Starving. And frankly. That suits you even better.

Beat.

So spotting an opportunity, you return, but this time you come in disguise. It's the same old colonial shit, just dressed in the shiny drag of free-market capitalism, eyes hard and dull as teeth.

Beat.

What did you offer us, Vivienne? When we were on our knees?

44

Abdi lurches up.

Abdi (*Somali*) *Muxuu yahay warkaad shubeysaan, soo baxa.* [Why all the talking? Come on.]

His jaw is loose, his eyes horribly bright.

Nala (*Somali*) *Waad ogayd qorshaha. Fariiso.* [You knew the plan. Sit down.]

Abdi stays standing. Edgy. Nala turns back to Vivienne.

Answer me.

Vivienne (*nervously watching Abdi*) I'm not sure I understand . . .

Abdi is fidgeting in the corner, licking his lips over and over.

Nala Yes, you do.

Vivienne I'm sorry, I really don't think I . . .

Nala You offered us aid, didn't you?

Vivienne Aid?

Nala To the camera.

Abdi is staring horribly hard at Robert.

Vivienne We offered Kenya aid. Yes.

Nala Why?

Vivienne Why? Well there were severe droughts –

Abdi stands suddenly. He's looking right at Robert.

Abdi (*Somali*) *Waxaan leeyahay ka'lab kaalaya aan sameynnee. Doofaarrayahow.* [I say let's just do it. Dogs.]

Frankie Mummy –

Nala (*Somali*) *Sug.* [Wait.]

Abdi looks at her, challenging.

(*Somali.*) *Ma dooneysaa lacagtaada fakin kaa mise maya?*
[Do you want your fucking money or not?]

> *He nods very slightly but remains standing, leaning
> against the wall, his fingers tapping his gun.*
> *Nala turns back to Vivienne.*

But the 'aid' you 'gave' us. It came with conditions,
didn't it?

Vivienne Yes. But that's very normal, most countries –

Nala But like you said, we were starving?

Vivienne I'm sorry, but I'm not sure what you're –

Nala Meaning we couldn't exactly refuse the aid, or the
'conditions' that came with it. They were tied up. Like
you. Am I right?

> *Beat.*
> *Vivienne is watching Abdi nervously, he is now
> staring at Frankie.*

Camera.

> *Vivienne looks at the camera.*

Vivienne The aid came with some . . . provisos, but I
promise you that's completely –

Nala What were those 'provisos', Vivienne?

> *She holds a gun to Robert's head.*

Chop-chop.

Frankie Answer her, Mummy.

Vivienne We encouraged certain . . . adjustments to help
liberalise your economy.

Nala Like privatisation and deregulation? Particularly of
the flower industry? Am I correct?

46

*Abdi takes khat out of a pouch and starts to chew it.
He doesn't take his eyes off Frankie.*

Vivienne Yes.

Nala And what does privatisation and deregulation
mean? To the average young . . . Jenny or Abdul who will
watch this tomorrow? Go on. More.

Vivienne It means lots of things. It means . . . It . . .
encourages foreign investment. So more money. It means
. . . improving standards of living for millions of people.
So, things like longer life-expectancy, better water
sanitation. And also, very importantly, increasing access
to female education –

Abdi fidgets, pacing.

Nala But that's a wide shot, isn't it? The big perspective.
What happened on the ground? In the factories? On the
farms? What happened there?

Ralph stirs.

Robert Ralph?

Nala spins around.

Nala SHUT UP!

Beat.

Answer me.

Vivienne Companies became . . . more efficient,
employment . . . boomed. More jobs were created –

Nala But it also meant no rules, right? No set standard
of conditions. No . . . rights.

Vivienne says nothing.

The minimum wage. A big achievement in Great Britain.
What happened to that?

Vivienne says nothing.

Ears . . .

Beat.

Vivienne That's not something a foreign government can enforce. Our powers are limited to our own country –

Nala Crowded concrete cells, hands warped from repetitive work, the constant threat of being sacked. No electricity, no running water, Parents forced to leave their children like dogs in filthy childcare units. All for what . . . Fifty pence a day?

She lightly touches the empty can from the minibar as she looks at them.

Very clever, I'll give you that. Instead of coming over with chains, this time you got us to enslave ourselves.

Vivienne We encouraged changes because we wanted to get your country and others like it to a position where your economy was so strong you wouldn't need any aid at all. We were trying to make you self-sufficient, the very opposite of enslaving you –

Nala But you profited. Heavily. From the changes you forced us to make. You're stealing from us, again, just this time –

Vivienne People were dying. Millions were starving. We had to do something. What would have happened if we hadn't? What would have happened to those people if we hadn't helped when we did?

Nala But you were the ones who pushed us to our knees in the first place. And as you helped us up you had a hand in our pocket. That isn't *help*. That's just another way of fucking us, but this time we're meant to be . . . what . . . grateful?

Vivienne It just isn't that black and white.

Beat. Nala lets it land.

Nala But it is though. Isn't it?

Beat.

What else was deregulated, Vivienne? Because of the
order you signed. What else specifically?

Vivienne There were many, which one –

Nala Ever heard of Aldrin, Lindane, DDT? You must
have heard of DDT. But maybe not, because of course
they're banned in Great Britain. Not in Kenya though.
Because the order you signed led to the removal of
import regulations. Which makes it very easy for
hazardous pesticides to be used, unchecked, on Kenyan
flower farms. In whatever toxic cocktail is cheapest.

Beat.

Poisonous pesticides for perfect roses.

Beat.

The irony of that is so fucking obvious it isn't even irony
any more. Is it? Did you or did you not sign that order?

Abdi (*Somali*) *Naayah, daaqo.* [Hurry up, come on.]

*Vivienne clears her throat. When she speaks it's slow.
Careful.*

Vivienne Yes. I did sign that order. But that order was a
small part of something much larger, many countries, the
World Bank, the IMF, were working hard together to –

Nala I see. It wasn't just you. You were just one face,
part of something much bigger?

Vivienne In effect, yes.

Beat.

Nala A many-headed monster doesn't care about consequences, does it? It doesn't need to. It's too big. A Hydra. Almost indestructible.

Beat.

If you cut one of the heads off a Hydra, two grow back. So the only way to truly kill such a monster is to burn each . . . stump.

Vivienne On my life, I swear, we did it for good.

Nala Do you know what a cocktail of those chemicals can do to the hands, the fingers? It's as though you are watching someone begin to decompose. The skin starts to discolour. Fingernails break, then drop off.

She speaks directly to Frankie

Imagine your mother, that warm body, that safe place, start to jerk and retch, coughing blood, covered in sweat. And there's nothing you can do but watch. Your hands are tied. I watched her begin to rot in front of me.

Beat.

That part of your career was considered hugely successful, wasn't it?

Abdi hears something. He springs up.

Abdi (*Somali*) *Wax baan maqlay; miyaanan maqal –* [I heard something, should I –]

Nala (*Somali*) *Sug.* [Wait.]

She turns back to Vivienne.

You've done well since then. Lovely house in Islington. Kids at good schools. Food on the table. Skulls under your feet.

Nala hears the sound.

(*Somali.*) *Halkaan joo.* [Stay here.]

She exits to investigate.

Vivienne Ralph?

Abdi points his gun at them.

Abdi (*Somali*) *Shib dheh.* [Shut up.]

Robert (*softly*) He's still out.

Vivienne (*softly*) Is everyone OK? Frankie.

Frankie isn't looking at her.

Frankie Did you know? About the pesticides?

Vivienne I had no idea that what we did would lead to that.

Frankie What does that even mean?

Vivienne I would never . . . Frankie, it was very complicated. All I did, Frankie, was sign some pieces of paper that sent aid, that sent help. I was doing a *good* thing.

Beat.

Frankie People died.

Vivienne I . . . I am so sorry this has happened.

Robert Bit late for that now, isn't it?

Beat. He regrets the awful joke.

Vivienne You have no idea, do you? Politics isn't a crusade, Robert. I'm not Robin Hood. I did my *best*. I'm not perfect. I'm sorry.

Beat.

Robert I love you.

They lock eyes. Nala re-enters. Vivienne nods at him,
she mouths 'I love you too'.
    The room is very dark now. There is a flash of
lightning. A roll of thunder. The storm is picking up
pace. Abdi starts a rhythm. He murmurs a child-
soldier battle chant. His eyes are closed. His voice soft.

Abdi (*Somali*) *Ka laya, ka laya u gaardiya dadka miidda*
ku joogadey ha ka walwahina janah sugeysa. [Come on,
come on. March on, those who step on mines will go to
paradise.]

Nala watches Abdi for a moment, then turns to them.

Nala I prefer real magic. Turning one thing into another.
Something. To something else. I had a thought, you see,
and I turned it into . . .

    She rummages in the laundry bag.
        She pulls out a large can of chemical fluid.
        Beat. They take it in. Abdi continues to chant.
        Frankie misreads it as a prayer, She turns to Nala,
desperate.

Frankie But what about your god? What about those
consequences?

Nala That's a little bit racist, isn't it? You assume I'm the
one with a god. That I'm the one drunk on hocus pocus
when actually it's her who worships blindly something
that's man-made and bigger than itself . . .

    She comes closer to Frankie, talking directly to her.

Because the thing is, when you turn the colour. The heat
of a human animal into a body. A corpse. And then you
take that corpse. That dead meat. And reduce it into a
cold curled swoop of a number. A symbol. A shape on a
page. Well. It's a second death. Isn't it? If one death tests

the idea of a god. Two can have all sorts of . . .
implications . . . We're our own gods now.

She puts on the gloves.

Did you know that skin pops, actually splutters when it
burns? I never knew that. The first time my new parents
gave me Rice Krispies I smashed the bowl. The flames
were different colours. Like a rainbow in hell.

Beat.

Because as you can imagine . . .

Nala pours a little into a bowl.

This stuff is pretty fucking flammable.

She lights it. The bowl flames, then subsides.
    *She starts to decant the rest of the chemical fluid
into a larger industrial spray can.*

And if it bleeds, it leads. So give the people what they
want and while they look, tell them the truth. Because
people like to watch hell . . .

*All the characters break the fourth wall and stare
directly at the audience for a second.*

Don't they?

*They turn back. She hears another sound. She glances
at Abdi.*
    *Another sound. Nala nods for Abdi to go out the
front. He does.*
    *She flicks the lights off. There is a sudden sound
from the back.*

Stay. Here.

Beat. Nala exits.
    The family wait a moment. Then Ralph sits up.
    They talk in hushed whispers.

Vivienne Quickly, quickly, untie Ralph.

Ralph sits up. They try and untie each other. It is agonising. We can hear Nala and Abdi prowling outside.

Ralph It won't –

Ralph nods, concentrating on freeing himself.

Frankie I think they're coming back –

Vivienne Keep trying –

Robert No. Lie back down –

He's nearly there.

Ralph Come on, come on.

Vivienne It might be people coming to help –

Robert (*harsh whisper*) And it might be someone even worse. *Lie back down!*

Ralph resumes his position, his hands still bound. But only just.

Ralph, I want you to know I'm sorry. For before. Truly sorry –

Nala and Abdi re-enter.

Frankie What was it?

Nala Fuck. The smell really lingers, doesn't it? Smells like home.

Beat.

Although it's not exactly the same. I could only get concentrate.

Nala dilutes fluid and puts it into the industrial-sized spray.

(*Somali.*) *Halkaas keen iyada hadda.* [Get her up here now.]

Vivienne I'm sorry, for everything. So sorry. But it wasn't their fault. It was me. Please let them go. Please –

Nala Some deaths are small, aren't they? Too small to really register. But others are . . . big. They get sprawled across newspapers. Splayed across screens. Forensic. Gory in their detail. Small deaths. Small lives. But you.

She looks directly at Vivienne.

Big.

She sprays their faces. She waits for their howls to subside before continuing.

Frankie STOP. Please STOP.

Robert Frankie, close your *eyes*.

Vivienne I can help. I can help you –

Nala You are helping me. Because I need to make this big. I have to make the small big. I need to burn their shapes into the sky. I want to tear new clouds. And to do that I need a big pig head on a big pig's plate, and that pig is you.

She soaks them both.

Vivienne I beg you. Stop. Please. Take her into another room. I'm sorry.

Nala What does that sorry even mean? It's just a word, isn't it?

Vivienne I'm sorry, I'm sorry.

Nala Just slipping . . . sliding . . . semantics.

Vivienne Please, I'm begging you. Close your eyes, Frankie. Please. *Please.* Look at her.

Nala I was her.

Vivienne I'm sorry, I'm fucking sorry –

Nala I don't want sorry. It's too late for sorry. I want you to acknowledge to the world what you have created. What your greed has done.

She lights a match.
   Vivienne stares at Frankie. She is ashen. Rocking slightly.
   She looks at Nala. Then Frankie again.

Vivienne I see it. I do.

Gestures to the camera.

Nala To the world. These things of darkness.

Vivienne These things of darkness.

Nala I acknowledge mine.

Vivienne I acknowledge mine.

Abdi sees something outside. He turns towards it. Seeing that he is distracted, Ralph leaps up and tackles him to the floor. The CD player is knocked over, 'I Get Around' by The Beach Boys blares, skipping and jumping. Lightning flashes. Images of the action get caught, like photographs, in the flashes of light.
   Abdi's gun rolls towards Frankie, who having freed herself, springs up and grabs it. Abdi charges her. She picks up the gun and shoots Abdi in the chest.
   Abdi falls to the floor. Blood runs from his mouth.
   Frankie turns to Nala. She hesitates. The doors are kicked open. Six Somalian Pirates charge the room. Guns out. Frankie runs through the doors out into the night. The room is trashed. Vivienne and Robert are taken. Ralph escapes.
   The song finishes. One Pirate remains. He takes in the room. Nala cowers in the corner.

Pirate (*Somali*) *Waa xaflad heer sare ah.* [Quite the party.]

Nala says nothing.

(*Somali*) *Gabadhii meeday?* [Where are the kids?]

Nala replies in English.

Nala What have you done? We had a deal.

The Pirate turns as if to go. As casually as waving goodbye, he turns round and shoots her.

Blackout.

Act Three

Half an hour later. The room is dark but the night is clear, still. The storm has finally subsided. Moonlight cuts across the floor.

Ralph enters. His arms and legs are scratched but he is otherwise unharmed. He turns on a light. He surveys the detritus. Objects have been knocked over, smashed. Their suitcases gutted. The laundry trolley is upended. The sheets tossed in a mound in the corner. Abdi's body is slumped face down. Otherwise the room appears empty.

Ralph opens the minibar; he gulps a bottle of water, the excess running down his face. He picks up the jelly beans. He puts them back in the minibar.

He goes and puts a towel over Abdi. Despite himself he looks directly at him. He throws up in the corner of the room.

He hears a sound. He freezes. Then another. It could be an animal. It's coming from the corner of the room. Another sound. He steps closer. He gulps.

Another sound. Ralph looks at the pile of sheets. He steps forward. Terrified.

He rips the sheets away. A small body is curled up, face hidden, wrapped in Frankie's sarong.

Ralph Frankie.

He kneels and turns the body gently. It is Nala. The sarong is bloody. He springs back. Nala pulls herself upwards slowly. They stare at each other for a moment.

Where's my sister?

Nala swallows. When she speaks, she speaks slowly. She is in pain.

Nala She ran. I thought you followed –

Ralph I lost her. I couldn't see. I just ran and ran and ran.

Nala I thought she was with you –

Ralph Who were those men?

Nala I don't –

Ralph WHO?

Nala They didn't do what they promised. We had a deal.

   Beat.

Look, they won't kill your parents. They won't be worth anything that way.

Ralph How do you know that?

Nala Because no one is worth anything as a hostage dead.

Ralph Well, you were wrong about your (*acid*) deal. So how do I know you're not FUCKING WRONG ABOUT THAT AS WELL? I only saw two shapes being taken on to that boat. And I've looked everywhere on this whole godforsaken hell rock of an island. *Everywhere.* So. If my sister isn't here. Or in the boat. Where. Is. She?

Nala How can I know –

Ralph BECAUSE YOU DID THIS! So tell me what's happening.

   His voice cracks.

Please.

   She tries to move. It hurts to.

Don't move. Don't you fucking move.

   He starts searching the room.

Where's the other gun?

59

Nala Frankie had –

Ralph Don't say her name.

Beat.

His gun.

He points at dead Abdi, but doesn't look directly at him.

Where is it?

Nala They took everything.

He searches the room. There is no sign of the gun but he spots the video camera on the floor.

Ralph Not everything.

He picks it up.
   Ralph turns on the camera and watches some playback. It sounds tinny and small in the empty room. He switches it off and looks up at her slowly. He sets the camera down on the table then stands up. He picks up the abandoned pesticide can. There is some left. He looks at her. He seems to consider it. With his other hand he starts collecting books, clothes, magazines. He makes a pile.

Nala What are you doing?

Ralph If I make a fire, Frankie might see. Someone might see.

Nala What if they come back?

Ralph I'll take the chance.

The camera is on the table. Ralph keeps adding to his pile. While he is distracted Nala attempts to lunge for the camera. The pain catches her by surprise. Ralph shoves her down. He pins her to the floor. She cowers.

I said don't move.

Beat. He takes her in.

Nala Please give me the camera.

Pause. He turns. He pours the pesticides on to the pile. He smells the air.

Ralph I can smell something. Something else. Can you?

Nala No.

Ralph I can, I really can.

He can't look at Abdi.

Matches – where are the fucking matches?

He swerves around to face her.

You had some at one point.

Beat.

Obviously.

Beat.

Where are they?

Nala I don't know –

Ralph Give me the fucking matches.

Nala I don't have them.

Ralph I don't believe you.

Ralph goes over to search her. He finds the matches in her pocket. As he does he sees that she's bleeding badly.

Fuck.

Beat.

That's bad, isn't it? Fuck.

He steps back.

Nala I need something to stop the bleeding.

Beat.

I can't do it myself.

Pause. He stares at her.
He lights the fire. The flames illuminate his face.

Ralph When I was little. All I wanted to be was a pirate.
I had a patch and everything. Frankie too. That's fucking
ironic.

Nala hums under her breath: 'How much is that puppy
in the window'.
Ralph turns and stares at her.

What?

Nala You said glass. I thought shop. Then that song just.

Ralph I didn't say any of those things.

Nala Oh.

She tails off.
Ralph stands up. He starts ripping a sheet.
Wordlessly he sits behind her and starts to bind the
wound. The action is perversely intimate. They don't
speak. When he's done he moves far away from her.

Thank you –

Ralph What if no one comes . . . We could be here for
days, couldn't we? Living off –

He pulls himself up and examines the minibar.

– jelly beans and vodka.

Beat.

Fuck it.

He opens the vodka.
Pause. He drinks.

Were you paying him?

She doesn't reply.

You were, weren't you?

Beat.

Buying him. Selling us.

Nala It was a job, I didn't buy him.

Ralph So you outsourced, did you? Delegated, was it? Come over from England and get a local to do your dirty work? Of course you didn't buy him.

Nala He wasn't local. He was Somalian. He ran away.

Ralph Well, whatever he was. Whatever it was. Like you give a fuck.

Beat.

You fucking hypocrite.

Beat.

You grew up in London, didn't you? Look at him. Go on.

He half drags her to Abdi's body. She yelps in pain.

Look at what you've fucking done.

Nala Get off me.

Ralph Fucking look. I just saved your life. Fucking look what could have happened to you.

Nala Am I meant to be grateful?

Ralph Excuse me?

Nala You only want me alive so you feel clean. So you can be some sort of . . . hero. Kill me if you want to. Don't if you don't. I don't owe you fucking anything.

Ralph has stood slowly.

Ralph What did you say?

Nala I said I don't owe you fucking anything.

He is close to her. He can't control himself. He kicks at her. Hard. And again. Again. With one foot he presses down on her injury.
Nala screams.
He stands back.
Stunned by himself.
Pause.
She has curled into herself. She moans.
She starts to cry.

Ralph No. Don't do that. Don't.

Beat.

STOP CRYING.

He smacks 'play' on the CD player. The same song as before blares loudly, then sparks and stops.
It blows a fuse. The lights cut. The theatre goes to emergency lighting.
The rest of the scene is played out in this state.
Ralph watches her for a moment, then gets a bottle of water from the minibar. He rolls it towards her. He sits down.
There is a sudden shot. The door kicks open, a figure stands there. Frankie is covered in mud. She looks wild. Animal. She holds the gun.

JESUS CHRIST! Frankie, stop.

She steps closer.

Frankie She deserves it. She fucking deserves it.

Ralph No. We're better than her.

Frankie doesn't move.

It's not worth it, Frankie.

There is the sound of an engine.

Frankie Look, there's a light.

Ralph Where?

She points.

I can see it. It's a boat. It could be help.

Frankie Or them. Again.

Ralph puts out the fire. Frankie turns to Nala, then back to Ralph. Their eyes lock.

No one would know.

The boat continues to roar towards them. The light gets brighter. Blinding.

The End.